# ICE Arbitration Procedure

## Third Edition

## Institution of Civil Engineers

The latest amendments to this document are available
as free downloads from www.ice.org.uk/law

## February 2006

Published by Thomas Telford Publishing, Thomas Telford Ltd, 1 Heron Quay, London E14 4JD
on behalf of

The Director General and Secretary
Institution of Civil Engineers
One Great George Street
London SW1P 3AA

Dispute Resolution Panel
Institution of Civil Engineers
One Great George Street
London SW1P 3AA

The Disputes Administration Service
Institution of Civil Engineers
One Great George Street
London SW1P 3AA


Third edition published February 2006

The Institution of Civil Engineers has as the sponsoring body, approved this new document. The Dispute Resolution Panel will keep under review the use of the document and consider any suggestions for amendment, which should be addressed to the ICE Secretariat, Institution of Civil Engineers, One Great George Street, London SW1P 3AA. A revision to the document will be made when such action seems warranted.

9 8 7 6 5 4 3 2 1

ISBN 0 7277 3465 2

Typeset by Academic + Technical, Bristol
Printed and bound in Great Britain by Formara Ltd., Southend-on-Sea

# Contents

## Acknowledgements

The Arbitration Procedure (2006) has been produced by the Institution of Civil Engineers through its Arbitration Advisory Panel.

Based on the Arbitration Procedure (1997), which was drafted by Mr Guy Cottam with the assistance of Mr Geoffrey Hawker, the Arbitration Procedure (2006) was drafted by Mr Guy Cottam (Chairman), Mr Geoffrey Hawker and Mr Alan Turner.

The original Arbitration Procedure (1983) was drafted by Mr Geoffrey Hawker, Professor John Uff and Mr Charles Timms.

Members of the Arbitration Advisory Panel were:

Mr J N Tait (Chairman) MA CEng FICE FCIArb
Mr G D G Cottam BSc(Eng) CEng FICE FIEI FCIArb MAE
Mr B S C Holloway MSc(Construction Law) LLB(Hons) CEng FICE FCIArb Barrister (non-practising)
Mr G Hawker TD BSc(Eng) FEng FICE CEng FIEI FIStructE MSocIS(France) MConsE FCIArb EurIng Barrister
Mr M D Joyce BSc MSc CEng CGeol FICE MAE FGS FCIArb Chartered Arbitrator
Mr D J Loosemore CEng FICE MCIArb FInstCES
Mr A J Turner BSc MSc LLB CEng FICE FCIArb MCIWEM Barrister
Mr A W Wood BSc CEng FICE FCIArb Dip Law Barrister (non-practising) Chartered Arbitrator.

ICE Secretariat
Mr J Hawkins (Group Manager) BA(Hons) MSc
Mr B van Rooyen

Although this Procedure has been prepared by the Institution of Civil Engineers principally for use with the ICE Conditions of Contract family and NEC Contracts in England and Wales for arbitrations conducted under the Arbitration Act 1996. It is suitable for use with other contracts and in other jurisdictions.

## Institution of Civil Engineers Arbitration Procedure (2006)

### Part A. Objectives, Reference and Appointment

**Rule 1. Aims and objectives**

1.1 The object of arbitration is to obtain the fair resolution of disputes by an impartial Arbitrator without unnecessary delay or expense. The Arbitrator shall give each party a reasonable opportunity of putting its case and dealing with that of its opponent.

1.2 Where the Act applies, the Rules of this Procedure are institutional rules for the purposes of s4 (3).

1.3 Except where there are express modifications in the Contract, or in the arbitration agreement, no alterations shall be made to this Procedure without the consent of the Arbitrator.

1.4    (a) Where the total of the sums claimed is within Band A, **Part F – Short Procedure** and all other Parts except Parts B, D, E and G shall apply.
   (b) Where the total sum of the sums claimed is within Band B, **Part G – Expedited Procedure** and all other Parts except Parts D, E and F shall apply.
   (c) Where the total sum of the sums claimed is within Band C all other Parts except Parts F and G shall apply.
   (d) Where the reference only contains declarations of principle **Part G – Expedited Procedure** and all other Parts except Parts D, E and F shall apply.
   (e) The parties may agree to depart from the foregoing provisions and adopt a different procedure, but only after the dispute has been referred to the Arbitrator and then only with leave.
   (f) The Bands applicable to the arbitration shall be those shown in Table 1 current at the time of the appointment of the Arbitrator.

1.5 The parties shall agree the seat of the arbitration. If the parties fail to agree the seat of the arbitration the seat shall be determined by the Arbitrator.

**Rule 2. Commencement of arbitration**

2.1 Unless otherwise provided in the contract, a dispute or difference shall be deemed to arise when a claim or assertion made by one party is rejected by the Other Party and either that rejection is not accepted or no response thereto is received within a period of 28 days. Subject only to the due observance of any condition precedent in the contract or the arbitration agreement, either party may then invoke arbitration by serving a Notice to Refer on the Other Party.

**Notice to Refer**

2.2 The date upon which the Notice to Refer is served shall be deemed to be the date upon which the arbitral proceedings are commenced.

2.3 The Notice to Refer shall list the matters which the issuing party wishes to be referred to arbitration. Nothing stated in the Notice shall restrict that party as to the manner in which he subsequently presents his case.

**Rule 3. Appointment of sole Arbitrator by agreement**

3.1 At the same time as or after serving the Notice to Refer, either party may serve upon the other a Notice to Concur in the appointment of an Arbitrator, listing therein the names and addresses of one or more persons he proposes as Arbitrator.

3.2 Within 14 days after the service of the Notice to Concur the Other Party shall

   (a) agree in writing to the appointment of one of the persons listed therein, or
   (b) propose in like manner an alternative person or persons.

3.3 Once agreement has been reached, the claiming party shall write to the person so selected inviting him to accept the appointment enclosing a copy of the Notice to Refer and documentary evidence of the other party's agreement to his appointment.

3.4 If the person so invited accepts the appointment he shall notify the issuing party in writing and send a copy to the Other Party. The date of posting or service, as the case may be, of this notification shall be deemed to be the date on which the Arbitrator's appointment is completed.

**Rule 4. Appointment of sole Arbitrator by the President**

4.1 If, within 21 days from the service of the Notice to Concur, the parties fail to appoint an Arbitrator in accordance with Rule 3 either party may then apply to the President to appoint an Arbitrator.

4.2 The application shall be in writing and should normally be accompanied by:

   (a) a copy of the Notice to Refer;
   (b) a copy of the Notice to Concur (if any);
   (c) the names and addresses of all parties to the arbitration;
   (d) a brief statement of the nature and circumstances of the dispute;
   (e) a copy of the arbitration clause in the contract or of the arbitration agreement;
   (f) the appropriate fee;
   (g) confirmation that any conditions precedent to arbitration contained in the contract or arbitration agreement have been complied with; and
   (h) any other relevant documents.

A copy of the application shall be sent at the same time to the Other Party.

Nothing stated in the application or in any supporting documentation shall restrict either party as to the manner in which he subsequently presents his case, nor shall it in any way restrict or delimit the scope of the reference or the Arbitrator's jurisdiction.

4.3 The President shall, within 14 days of receiving the application or within such further time as may be necessary, make the appointment and the Arbitrator's appointment shall thereby be completed. The Institution will notify both parties and the Arbitrator in writing as soon as possible thereafter.

Provided always that no such appointment shall be invalidated merely because the time limits set out herein have not been observed.

**Rule 5. Notice of further disputes of differences**

5.1 At any time before the Arbitrator's appointment is completed, either party may put forward further disputes or differences to be referred to him by serving upon the Other Party an additional Notice to Refer in accordance with Rule 2.

5.2 Once his appointment is completed the Arbitrator shall have jurisdiction over any issue connected with and necessary to the determination of any dispute or difference already referred to him whether or not any condition precedent to referring the matter to arbitration had been complied with.

## Part B. Arrangements for the Arbitration

**Rule 6. The preliminary meeting**

6.1 The Arbitrator may, upon appointment, require the parties to submit to him short statements expressing their perceptions of the disputes or differences. Such statements shall give sufficient detail of the nature of the issues to enable the Arbitrator and the parties to discuss appropriate procedures for the preliminary meeting.

6.2 After accepting the appointment, the Arbitrator may as soon as reasonably practical summon the parties to a preliminary meeting for the purpose of giving such directions about the Procedure to be adopted in the arbitration as he considers necessary and dealing with the matters referred to in Rule 6.1.

6.3 If the parties so wish, they may themselves agree directions and submit them in draft to the Arbitrator for his approval which shall not unreasonably be withheld. In so doing the parties shall consider all the matters referred to in Rule 6.4 and shall state whether or not they wish Part F or Part G or Part H of these Rules to apply.

6.4 The parties and the Arbitrator shall consider whether and to what extent:

(a) Part F (Short Procedure), Part G (Expedited Procedure) or Part H (Special Procedure for Experts) of these Rules shall apply;

(b) progress may be facilitated and costs saved by determining some of the issues in advance of the main hearing;

(c) evidence of Experts may be necessary or desirable;

(d) disclosure of documents should be ordered;

(e) there should be a limit put on Recoverable Costs; and

(f) where the Act applies to the Arbitration, the parties should enter into an agreement (if they have not already done so) excluding the right to appeal in accordance with ss32, 45 and 69 of the Act,

and in general shall consider such other steps as may achieve the speedy and cost effective resolution of the disputes.

## Part C. Control of the Proceedings

**Rule 7. Power to control the proceedings**

7.1 The Arbitrator may exercise any or all of the powers set out or necessarily to be implied in this Procedure on such terms as he thinks fit, and the parties shall not deny that the Arbitrator has such powers.

**Jurisdiction**

7.2 The Arbitrator shall have power to rule on his own substantive jurisdiction and in particular as to:

(a) whether there is a valid arbitration agreement;

(b) whether he is properly appointed;

(c) whether there is a dispute or difference capable of being referred to arbitration;

(d) whether the dispute has been validly referred; and

(e) what matters have been submitted in accordance with the arbitration agreement and this Procedure.

7.3 Should any party refer a ruling under Rule 7.2 to the court, the Arbitrator shall direct whether or not the arbitral proceedings shall continue pending a decision by the court.

**General**

7.4 The Arbitrator shall have power to decide all procedural and evidential matters including but not limited to:

(a) whether any, and if so what, form of written statements of claim and defence are to be used, when these should be supplied and the extent to which such statements can later be amended;

(b) whether any, and if so which, documents or classes of document should be disclosed between and produced by the parties and at what stage;

(c) whether any, and if so what, questions should be put to and answered by the respective parties in advance of a hearing and when and in what form this should be done;

(d) whether to apply the strict rules of evidence (or any other rules) as to the admissibility, relevance or weight of any material (oral, written or other) sought to be tendered on any matters of fact or opinion, and the time, manner and form in which such material should be exchanged and presented;

(e) whether and to what extent the Arbitrator should himself take the initiative in ascertaining the facts and the law;

(f) whether to rely upon his own knowledge and expertise to such extent as he thinks fit;

(g) whether and to what extent there should be oral or written evidence or submissions;

(h) whether and to what extent Expert evidence should be adduced;

(i) whether and to what extent evidence should be given under oath or affirmation;

(j) the manner in which the evidence of witnesses shall be taken; and

(k) whether translations of any relevant documents are to be supplied:

and in default of agreement between the parties, shall have power to decide:

(l) when and where any part of the proceedings is to be held; and

(m) the language or languages to be used in the proceedings.

**Non-compliance with orders**

7.5 The Arbitrator shall have power to give orders and directions in respect of:

(a) the time for compliance and the consequences of non-compliance with orders and directions;

(b) the conducting of enquiries, tests or investigations which the Arbitrator may require; and

(c) the recognition or disallowance of any level of representation in the determination of costs.

7.6 Should any party fail to comply with any direction given in accordance with this Procedure such inferences may be drawn therefrom as seems to the Arbitrator both reasonable and just.

**Use of assessors and seeking outside advice**

7.7 The Arbitrator may appoint a legal, technical or other assessor to assist him in the conduct of the arbitration. The Arbitrator shall direct when such assessor is to attend hearings of the arbitration.

7.8 The Arbitrator may seek legal, technical or other advice on any matter arising out of or in connection with the proceedings. The parties shall be given a reasonable opportunity to comment on any information, opinion or advice offered by any such person.

7.9 All cost arising from the Arbitrator's actions under Rules 7.7 and 7.8 shall be costs in the arbitration.

**Security for costs**

7.10 The Arbitrator shall have power to:

(a) direct that the Recoverable Costs of the arbitration be limited to a specified amount;

(b) order the deposit of money or other security to secure the whole or any part of the amount(s) in dispute;

(c) make an order for security for costs in favour of one or more of the parties; and

(d) order his own costs to be secured.

Money ordered to be paid under this Rule shall be paid without delay into a separate bank account in the name of a stakeholder to be appointed by and subject to the directions of the Arbitrator.

**Protective measures**    7.11    The Arbitrator (and in the case of urgency the courts also) shall have power to:

(a) order the preservation of evidence;
(b) make orders relating to property which is the subject of the proceedings or as to which any question arises in the proceedings:
  (i) for the inspection, photographing, preservation, custody or detention of the property, or
  (ii) ordering that samples be taken from, or any observation be made of or experiment conducted upon, the property; and
(c) give directions for the detention, storage, sale or disposal of the whole or any part of the subject matter of the dispute at the expense of one or both of the parties.

## Part D. Procedures Before the Hearing

**Rule 8. Statements of case and disclosure of documents**    8.1    Unless the Arbitrator otherwise directs, each party shall prepare in writing and shall serve upon the Other Party or parties and the Arbitrator a statement of their case comprising:

(a) a summary of that party's case;
(b) a summary of that party's evidence;
(c) a statement or summary of the issues between the parties;
(d) a list and/or a summary of the documents relied upon;
(e) any points of law with references to any authorities relied upon;
(f) a statement or summary of any other matters likely to assist the resolution of the disputes or differences between the parties; and
(g) any other document or statement that the Arbitrator considers necessary.

The Arbitrator may order any party to answer the Other Party's case and to give reasons for any disagreement therewith.

8.2    Statements or answers shall contain sufficient detail for the Other Party to know the case he has to answer. If sufficient detail is not provided the Arbitrator may of his own motion or at the request of the Other Party order the provision of such further information, clarification or elaboration as he may think fit.

8.3    The Arbitrator may order any party to deliver either with its statement of case or otherwise any documents in his possession, custody or power which relate either generally or specifically to matters in issue, or upon which he intends to rely.

8.4    (1) If a party fails to comply with any order made under this rule the Arbitrator may issue a peremptory order to the same effect directing such time for compliance as the Arbitrator considers appropriate.

**ICE Arbitration Procedure (2006)**

(2) If the defaulting party fails to comply with a peremptory order the Arbitrator shall have power to:

    (a) debar that party from relying on the matters in respect of which he is in default;

    (b) draw such adverse inferences from the act of non-compliance as the circumstances justify; and

    (c) proceed to an award on the basis of such materials as have been properly provided to him;

provided that the Arbitrator shall first give notice to the party in default that he intends to proceed under this rule.

8.5     If the Arbitrator is satisfied that there has been inordinate and inexcusable delay by either party in pursuing his claim (or counter-claim) and that delay:

    (a) gives rise or is likely to give rise to substantial risk that it is not possible to have a fair resolution of the issues in that claim; or

    (b) has caused or is likely to cause, serious prejudice to the other party;

then the Arbitrator may make an award dismissing the claim.

**Rule 9. Power to order concurrent Hearings**

9.1     Where disputes or differences have arisen under two or more contracts, each concerned wholly or mainly with the same subject matter, and the resulting arbitrations have been referred to the same Arbitrator, he may with the agreement of all the parties concerned or upon the application of one of the parties being a party to all the contracts involved, order that the whole or any part of the matters at issue shall be heard together upon such terms or conditions as the Arbitrator thinks fit.

9.2     Where an order for concurrent Hearings has been made under Rule 9.1, the Arbitrator shall nevertheless make and publish separate awards unless all the parties otherwise agree but the Arbitrator may, if he thinks fit, prepare one combined set of reasons to cover all the awards.

**Rule 10. Procedural meetings**

10.1     The Arbitrator may at any time call such procedural meetings as he deems necessary to identify or clarify the issues to be decided and the Procedures to be adopted. For this purpose, the Arbitrator may request particular persons to attend on behalf of the parties.

10.2     Either party may at any time apply to the Arbitrator for leave to appear before him on any interlocutory matter. The Arbitrator may call a procedural meeting for the purpose or deal with the application in correspondence or otherwise as he thinks fit.

10.3     At any procedural meeting or otherwise, the Arbitrator may give such directions as he thinks fit for the proper conduct of the arbitration.

© Institution of Civil Engineers 2006

**Rule 11. Preparation for the Hearing**

11.1 In addition to his other powers, the Arbitrator shall also have power to:

(a) order that the parties shall agree facts as facts and figures as figures where possible;

(b) order the parties to prepare an agreed and paginated bundle of all documents relied upon by the parties. The agreed bundle shall thereby be deemed to have been entered in evidence without further proof and without being read out at the Hearing. Provided always that either party may at the Hearing challenge the admissibility of any document in the agreed bundle; and

(c) direct that any Experts, whose reports have been exchanged before the Hearing, shall all meet and prepare a joint report identifying the points in issue and any other matters covered by their reports upon which they are in agreement and those upon which they disagree, stating the reasons for any disagreement.

11.2 Before the Hearing, the Arbitrator may and, if so requested by the parties, shall read the documents to be used at the Hearing. For this or any other purpose the Arbitrator may require all such documents to be delivered to him at such time and place as he may specify.

## Part E. Procedure at the Hearing

**Rule 12. Powers at the Hearing**

12.1 The Arbitrator may hear the parties, their representatives and/or witnesses at any time or place and may adjourn the arbitration for any period on the application of any party or as he thinks fit.

12.2 Any party may be represented by any person including, in the case of a company or other legal entity, a director, officer, employee or beneficiary of such company or entity. In particular, a person shall not be prevented from representing a party because he is or may be also a witness in the proceedings. Nothing shall prevent a party from being represented by different persons at different times.

12.3 Nothing in these Rules or in any other rule, custom or practice shall prevent the Arbitrator from starting to hear the arbitration once his appointment is completed or at any time thereafter.

12.4 Any meeting with or summons before the Arbitrator at which both parties are represented may, if the Arbitrator so directs, be treated as part of the Hearing of the arbitration.

12.5 At or before the Hearing and after hearing representations on behalf of each party the Arbitrator shall determine the order in which the parties shall present their cases and/or the order in which the issues shall be heard and determined.

12.6 Either party may make oral submissions to which the other party shall have the right to reply. The Arbitrator may order that such submissions shall be confirmed in writing.

12.7  The Arbitrator may at any time (whether before or after the Hearing has commenced) allocate the time available for the Hearing between the parties, and those representing the parties shall then adhere strictly to that allocation. Should a party's representative fail to complete the presentation of that party's case within the time so allowed, further time shall only be afforded at the sole discretion of the Arbitrator and upon such conditions as to costs as the Arbitrator may see fit to impose.

12.8  The Arbitrator may, on the application of either party or of his own motion, hear and determine any issue or issues separately.

12.9  If a party fails to appear at the Hearing and provided that the absent party has had notice of the Hearing or the Arbitrator is satisfied that all reasonable steps have been taken to notify him of the Hearing, the Arbitrator may proceed with the Hearing in his absence. The Arbitrator shall nevertheless take all reasonable steps to ensure that the disputes between the parties are determined justly and fairly.

**Rule 13. Evidence**

13.1  The Arbitrator may order a party to submit in advance of the Hearing a list of the witnesses he intends to call. That party shall not thereby be bound to call any witness so listed and may add to the list so submitted at any time.

13.2  No Expert evidence shall be admissible except by leave of the Arbitrator. Leave may be given on such terms and conditions as the Arbitrator thinks fit. Unless the Arbitrator otherwise orders, such terms shall be deemed to include a requirement that a report from each Expert, containing the substance of the evidence to be given, shall be served upon the Other Party within a reasonable time before the Hearing.

13.3  The Arbitrator may order that Experts appear before him separately or concurrently at the Hearing so that he may examine them inquisitorially, provided always that at the conclusion of the questioning by the Arbitrator the parties or their representatives shall have the opportunity to put such further questions to any Expert as they may reasonably require.

13.4  The Arbitrator may order disclosure or exchange of proofs of evidence relating to factual issues. The Arbitrator may also order any party to prepare and disclose in writing in advance a list of points or questions to be put in cross-examination of any witness.

13.5  Where a list of questions is disclosed, whether pursuant to an order of the Arbitrator or otherwise, the party making disclosure shall not be bound to put any question therein to the witness unless the Arbitrator so orders. Where the party making disclosure puts a question not so listed in cross-examination, the Arbitrator may disallow the costs thereby occasioned.

13.6 The Arbitrator may order that any witness statement or Expert's report which has been disclosed shall stand as the evidence in chief of that witness or Expert, provided that the other party has been or will be given an opportunity to cross-examine the witness or Expert thereon. The Arbitrator may also, at any time before such cross-examination, order the witness or Expert to deliver written answers to questions arising out of any statement or report.

## Part F. Short Procedure

**Rule 14. Short Procedure**

14.1 Where Rule 1.4(a) applies, or where the parties so agree pursuant to Rule 6.4(a) (either of their own motion or at the invitation of the Arbitrator) the arbitration shall be conducted in accordance with the following Short Procedure.

**Statement of case**

14.2 Within 2 working days of the appointment of the arbitrator (or, if one has already been appointed, from the delivery of the Notice to Refer), the claiming party shall set out his case in the form of a file containing:

(a) a statement as to the orders or awards he seeks;
(b) a statement of his reasons for being entitled to such orders or awards; and
(c) copies of any documents on which he relies (including statements), identifying the origin and date of each document;

and shall deliver copies of the said file to the Other Party and to the Arbitrator in such manner and within such time as the Arbitrator may direct.

Provided that where this Procedure is adopted under Rules 1.4(e) and 6.4(a) the parties shall agree the date for the submission of the file.

14.3 The Responding Party shall, within 14 days of receipt of the claiming party's file, deliver to the claiming party and to the Arbitrator his defence to the claiming party's case in like form.

14.4 There shall be no counterclaim. Should the Responding Party wish to raise a counterclaim he must do so by way of a separate reference.

**Close of pleadings**

14.5 Following delivery of the Responding Party's file, under Rule 14.3 there shall be a period of 14 days during which the parties may comment on their opponent's file and/or add to or deduct from their own file.

Upon expiry of the said period of 14 days, both files shall be closed and no further comment shall be admissible.

**Award**

14.6 Within 14 days after closure of the files pursuant to Rule 14.5, the Arbitrator shall make and publish his Award. Provided that in his sole discretion the Arbitrator may extend this period of 14 days to accommodate the provisions of Rule 14.8.

10

**Costs**

14.7 Each party shall bear his own costs in the arbitration in any event, save that this Rule shall have no effect if dissented from in writing by either party within 10 days after delivery of the documents under 14.2.

14.8 Not withstanding the provisions of Rules 14.5 and 14.6 and in his own discretion the Arbitrator may:

(a) visit the Site or the Works;
(b) require either or both parties to submit further documents or information in writing;
(c) require the parties to attend a meeting for the purpose of answering the Arbitrator's questions put to them, their representatives or witnesses. Provided that the parties shall not themselves ask questions unless the Arbitrator so permits. Provided also that no person shall be bound to appear before him.

14.9 Neither party shall be entitled to a formal hearing or to examine or cross-examine witnesses or to make submissions other than in writing, unless the Arbitrator in his sole discretion gives leave.

Such leave shall be given only upon the condition that the requesting party bear the whole of any extra costs thereby incurred to himself, the other party and to the Arbitrator.

## Part G. The Expedited Procedure

**Rule 15. Service of pleadings**

15.1 Where Rule 1.4(b) or (d) applies or where the parties so agree pursuant to Rule 6.4(a) (either of their own motion or at the invitation of the Arbitrator), the arbitration shall be conducted in accordance with the following Expedited Procedure.

15.2 Within two working days of his appointment (or the adoption of this procedure if later) the Arbitrator shall establish and order a procedural timetable of no longer than 100 days to run from service of the statement of claim or from the date that the Arbitrator gives his directions (whichever is later).

15.3 The said timetable shall include:

(a) a date for service of the statement of claim (if not already served) as soon as possible;
(b) a date for service of the statement of defence within 21 working days thereafter;
(c) a date for service of the reply 14 working days thereafter;
(d) either:
(i) a date for an oral hearing not exceeding five working days to commence not more than 28 days after conclusion of the foregoing steps; or
(ii) final written submissions (if ordered by the Arbitrator) and submissions on costs to be served within five working days from the end of the hearing; or
(iii) final written submissions to be served within 10 working days from the expiry of the period allowed in Rule 15.3(c).

The Arbitrator may, if so agreed by the parties, direct shorter periods for any of the foregoing steps and the period of 100 days shall be reduced accordingly.

15.4 The Arbitrator, for the purpose of achieving the foregoing time limits, may do any of the following:

(a) order any submission or other material to be delivered in writing;

(b) take the initiative in ascertaining the facts and the law;

(c) direct the manner in which the time at the hearing is to be used;

(d) limit or specify the number of witnesses and/or Experts to be heard orally;

(e) order questions to witnesses or experts to be put and answered in writing;

(f) conduct the questioning of witnesses himself;

(g) require two or more witnesses to give their evidence together.

**Documents**

15.5 All submissions served in accordance with Rule 15.3 shall be accompanied by all supporting documents, statements of witnesses and Experts' reports relied on, and by requests for disclosure of specific documents by the Other Party.

15.6 Subject to any direction or ruling by the Arbitrator on any issue as to disclosure of documents, each party shall serve copies of the documents so requested within a further period of 14 days. No further documents may be served by either party unless requested by the Arbitrator.

**Confirmation of dates**

15.7 Upon completion of the steps set out in Rules 15.3 and 15.4, the Arbitrator shall confirm or vary the date or dates ordered under Rule 15.3(d).

**Award**

15.8 The Arbitrator shall make his award (including costs) within 18 days of the end of the oral hearing pursuant to Rules 15.3(d)(i) and (ii) or receipt of final submissions pursuant to rule 15.3(d)(iii) (as the case may be).

**Extension of time**

15.9 The parties may agree to extend the period of 100 days. The Arbitrator shall have no such power.

## Part H.  Special Procedure for Experts

**Rule 16. Special Procedure for Experts**

16.1 Where the parties so agree (either of their own motion or at the invitation of the Arbitrator) the hearing and determination of any issues of fact which depend upon the evidence of Experts shall be conducted in accordance with the following Special Procedure.

16.2 Each party shall set out his case on such issues in the form of a file containing:

(a) a statement of the factual findings he seeks;
(b) a report or statement from and signed by each Expert upon whom that party relies; and
(c) copies of any other documents referred to in each Experts report or statement or on which the party relies, identifying the origin and date of each document;

and shall deliver copies of the said file to the other party and to the Arbitrator in such manner and within such time as the Arbitrator may direct.

16.3 After reading the parties' cases the Arbitrator may view the site or the Works and may require either or both parties to submit further documents or information in writing.

16.4 Thereafter, the Arbitrator shall fix a day when he shall meet the Experts whose reports or statements have been submitted. At the meeting each Expert may address the Arbitrator and put questions to any other Expert representing the Other Party. The Arbitrator shall so direct the meeting as to ensure that each Expert has an adequate opportunity to explain his opinion and to comment upon any opposing opinion. No other person shall be entitled to address the Arbitrator or question any Expert unless the parties and the Arbitrator so agree.

16.5 Thereafter, the Arbitrator may make and publish an award setting out with such details or particulars as may be necessary his decision upon the issues dealt with.

**Rule 17. Costs**

17.1 The Arbitrator may in his award make orders as to the payment of any costs relating to the foregoing matters including his own fees and expenses in connection therewith.

17.2 Unless the parties otherwise agree and so notify the Arbitrator, neither party shall be entitled to any costs in respect of legal representation assistance or other legal work relating to the hearing and determination of factual issues by this Special Procedure.

## Part J. Awards

**Rule 18. Awards**

18.1 The Arbitrator may at any time make an award, and may make more than one award at different times on different aspects of the matters to be determined.

18.2    Awards may:

    (a)  order the payment of money to one or more of the parties;
    (b)  order a party to do or refrain from doing anything;
    (c)  order specific performance;
    (d)  make a declaration as to any matter to be determined;
    (e)  order rectification, setting aside or cancellation of a deed or other document;
    (f)  be a consent award in the event of a settlement, which shall include an allocation of the costs of the arbitration.

**Provisional relief**

18.3    The Arbitrator may also make an order for provisional relief and for this purpose the Arbitrator shall have power to award payment by one party to another of a sum representing a reasonable proportion of the final net amount which in his opinion that party is likely to be ordered to pay after determination of all the issues in the arbitration, and after taking into account any defence or counterclaim upon which the Other Party may be entitled to rely.

18.4    The Arbitrator shall have power to order the party against whom an order for provisional relief is made to pay part or all of the sum awarded to a stakeholder. In default of compliance with such an order, the Arbitrator may order payment of the whole sum in the order for provisional relief to the Other Party.

18.5    Unless the parties otherwise agree after the commencement of the arbitration, the Arbitrator shall have power to order payment of costs in relation to an order for provisional relief including power to order that such costs shall be paid forthwith.

18.6    An order for provisional relief shall be binding upon the parties unless and until it is varied by any subsequent award made and published by the same Arbitrator or by any other Arbitrator having jurisdiction over the matters in dispute. Any such subsequent award may order repayment of monies paid in accordance with the order.

**Interest**

18.7    In any award, the Arbitrator shall have power to award interest either simple or compound at such rate and between such dates as he thinks fit.

**Costs**

18.8    In any award, the Arbitrator shall have power to:

    (a)  allocate the costs of the arbitration between the parties in such manner as he considers appropriate;
    (b)  direct the basis upon which the costs are to be determined; and
    (c)  in the default of agreement by the parties, determine the amount of the Recoverable Costs.

**Rule 19. Reasons**

19.1    The Arbitrator shall include in his award reasons for the award, unless it is a consent award or the parties have agreed to dispense with reasons.

**Rule 20. Making the award**

20.1 Upon the closing of the hearing (if any) and after having considered all the evidence and submissions, the Arbitrator shall prepare and make his award.

20.2 When the Arbitrator has made his award or an order for provisional relief under Rule 18, he shall so inform the parties in writing and shall specify how and where it may be taken up upon full payment of his fees and expenses.

20.3 The Arbitrator may on the application of any party made within 28 days of the date of the award or on his own initiative:

    (a) correct an award so as to remove any clerical mistake or error arising from an accidental slip or omission, or clarify or remove any ambiguity in the award; or

    (b) make an additional award in respect of any claim (including a claim for loss of interest or costs) which was presented to him but was not dealt with in the award.

Such correction or additional award shall be made within 28 days of the date of the award or of receipt of the application (as the case may be).

**Rule 21. Appeals**

21.1 If any party applies to the court for leave to appeal against any award or decision or for an order staying the arbitration proceedings or for any other purpose that party shall forthwith notify the Arbitrator of the application.

The Arbitrator may continue the arbitral proceedings, including making further awards, pending a decision by the court.

21.2 Once any award or decision has been made and taken up the Arbitrator shall be under no obligation to make any statement in connection therewith other than in compliance with an order of the court under s70 (4) of the Act.

## Part K. Miscellaneous

**Rule 22. Definitions**

22.1 In these Rules the following definitions shall apply.

    (a) All references to days are references to Calendar Days unless otherwise stated.

    (b) 'Arbitrator' includes a tribunal of two or more Arbitrators or an Umpire.

    (c) 'Institution' means the Institution of Civil Engineers.

    (d) 'Responding Party' and 'Other Party' includes the plural unless the context otherwise requires.

    (e) 'President' means the President for the time being of the Institution or any Vice-President acting on his behalf or such other person as may have been nominated in the arbitration agreement to appoint the Arbitrator in default of agreement between the parties.

    (f) 'Procedure' means the Institution of Civil Engineers' Arbitration Procedure (2006) unless the context otherwise requires.

(g) 'Contract' means the contract between the parties which either incorporates the arbitration agreement or under which the dispute arises.

(h) 'Expert' means an expert witness or person called to give expert opinion evidence.

(i) The 'Act' means the Arbitration Act 1996 and when the Act applies words defined in it shall have the same meanings in this Procedure.

(j) 'Recoverable Costs' of the Arbitration shall include the parties' own legal and other costs incurred in preparing their cases, and preparing for and appearing at any hearing or other meeting.

(k) The 'Arbitrator's Costs' shall include his fees and expenses incurred on or in connection with the arbitration, and the fees and expenses of any advisor or assessor he may employ in accordance with this Procedure.

**Rule 23. Application of the ICE Procedure**

23.1 This Procedure shall apply to the conduct of the arbitration if:

(a) the contract so provides;
(b) the parties at any time so agree; or
(c) the Arbitrator so stipulates at the time of his appointment.

Provided that where this Procedure applies by virtue of the Arbitrator's stipulation under (c) above, the parties may within 14 days of that appointment agree otherwise, in which event the Arbitrator, may terminate his appointment and the parties shall pay his reasonable charges in equal shares.

23.2 This Procedure shall not apply to arbitrations under the law of Scotland for which a separate ICE Appendix to the Scottish Arbitration Code is available.

23.3 Where an arbitration is governed by the law of a country other than England and Wales or Northern Ireland, this Procedure shall apply to the extent that the applicable law permits.

23.4 If, after the appointment of the Arbitrator, any agreement is reached between the parties which is inconsistent with this Procedure the Arbitrator shall be entitled, upon giving reasonable notice, to terminate his appointment, and shall be entitled to payment of his reasonable fees and expenses incurred up to the date of the termination.

**Rule 24. Exclusion of liability**

24.1 Neither the Arbitrator nor any employee or agent of the Arbitrator shall be liable for anything done or omitted in the discharge or purported discharge of his functions as Arbitrator unless the act or omission is shown to have been in bad faith.

24.2 Neither the Institution nor its servants or agents nor the President shall be liable to any party for any act omission or misconduct in connection with any appointment made or any arbitration conducted under this Procedure.

Table 1

**Table 1 Value bands for procedure selection**

| Band | Total sum in issue |
|------|--------------------|
| A | Not exceeding £50,000 |
| B | £50,001 to £250,000 |
| C | Over 250,001 |

1 The Institution of Civil Engineers updates this Table from time to time.

2 The applicable version for use with the Institution of Civil Engineers' Arbitration Procedure 2006 is the version current at the appointment of Arbitrator.

3 The latest version of the Table can be downloaded from www.ice.org.uk/law

**Notice to Refer a Dispute to Arbitration**

To:     *(Name of Respondent)*
         *(Address of Respondent)*

Date:

**Notice to Refer**

*(Contract name)*

We consider that the following dispute(s) or difference(s) have arisen between us:

We now give notice that we require these dispute(s) or diffence(s) to be referred to arbitration.

Yours faithfully

For and on behalf of
*(Claimant's name)*

**Notice to Concur in the Appointment of an Arbitrator**

To:     *(Name of Respondent)*
        *(Address of Respondent)*

Date:

*(Title of dispute):*

Further to the **Notice to Refer** this dispute between us to arbitration given by us/you and dated (date), we now call upon you to concur in the appointment of an arbitrator to hear and determine the dispute(s) listed in the **Notice to Refer.**

We propose the following person for your consideration:

Name of the proposed Arbitrator:

Address:

And require you within 14 days of receipt of this notice to:

(a)  agree in writing to the appointment; or
(b)  propose an alternative person for our consideration

failing which we intend to apply to the President of the Institution of Civil Engineers to appoint an arbitrator.

Yours faithfully

For and on behalf of:
*(Name of applicant)*

**Our ref:**

Institution of Civil Engineers
One Great George Street
Westminster
London SW1P 3AA
United Kingdom

Refferring Party

**t** +44 (0)20 7665 2214
**f** +44 (0)20 7222 1403
**e** contractsanddisputes@ice.org.uk

www.ice.org.uk

Dear Sir or Madam

**Appointment of an Arbitrator by the President**

Further to your request, I enclose Form Arb(ICE) for you to complete should you require the appointment of an arbitrator by the President. A copy of the completed form should be sent to the respondents and the **original** returned to this office together with a cheque for £323.13 (£275 + VAT). You will also need to send copies of the Notice to Refer and Notice to Concur in accordance with the ICE Procedure, paragraph 4.2.

Please also send copies of letters to show that the parties have tried but failed to concur in the appointment of their own arbitrator.

Yours faithfully

Institution of Civil Engineers

Encl.

**Application for the Appointment of an Arbitrator by the President of the Institution of Civil Engineers**

Dispute Administration Service
Institution of Civil Engineers
1 Great George Street
Westminster
London SW1P 3AA                    Date: .......................

The dispute(s) and or difference(s) described in the Schedule have arisen and since the Parties have failed to agree a person I/we hereby apply to you to make an appointment.

I/we confirm that I/we have performed all the actions to be performed by me/us as required under the contract before I/we am/are entitled to apply to you to make an appointment.

I/we agree to meet all the reasonable costs incurred by the person appointed by you if I/we am/are not entitled to make this application in accordance with the agreement between the parties.

I/we enclose a cheque for the sum indicated in the letter "Appointment of an Arbitrator by the President" in respect of the charge made by the Institution towards the administrative cost in connection with this application.

Yours faithfully

For and on behalf of:

Name: ...............................................................................................................

Address: ............................................................................................................

.........................................................................................................................

.........................................................................................................................

Telephone: .............................................. Fax: ................................................

**Schedule to the Application for the Appointment by the President\* of the Institution of Civil Engineers**

**Referring Party** (if a representative has signed the application)

Name: ........................................................................................................................

Address: ....................................................................................................................

.................................................................................................................................

.................................................................................................................................

Telephone: ............................................... Fax: ...................................................

**Other Party**

Name: ........................................................................................................................

Address: ....................................................................................................................

.................................................................................................................................

.................................................................................................................................

Telephone: ............................................... Fax: ...................................................

**Other Party Representatives**

Name: ........................................................................................................................

Address: ....................................................................................................................

.................................................................................................................................

.................................................................................................................................

Telephone: ............................................... Fax: ...................................................

**The Contract**

Title of Contract:

Date of Contract:

Brief Description of the Contract Works:

**The Arbitration Agreement**

The agreement to arbitrate is found in *(Please state and attach a copy hereto):*

---

\* Delete when Institution is stipulated.

## The Dispute(s) or Difference(s)

Please give a brief description of the dispute(s) or difference(s) to be referred to the person appointed to assist the President in the choice.

Approximate value of amount in dispute (if appropriate): £ .....................

Please state whether the works are complete or not: ...........................

## The Appointee

Please state fields or professions in which you consider that it would be desirable for the arbitrator to be skilled or experienced.

## Notes

1    The President will make an appointment upon the application of any person using this form. He will not investigate the validity of the application.

2    In making this application the Applicant undertakes to meet the reasonable charges of the person appointed by the President/Institution pursuant to this application should the arbitration not proceed.

3    The brief description of the dispute(s) or difference(s) given above is for the use of the President/ Institution and shall not be taken in any way to define the scope of the reference and/or limit the jurisdiction of the person appointed.

4    The President/Institution is not bound by all or any of the requirements stated by the applicant.

5    Neither the Institution nor its servants or agents nor the President shall be liable to any party for any act, omission or misconduct in connection with any appointment made under this form.

## Arbitrator's Key Words

I require an Arbitrator with experience in the following type of construction activity (please tick as appropriate):

### Category A – Type of Construction Activity

☐ **Civil Engineering**    ☐ **Construction**    ☐ **Process Engineering**    ☐ **Specialist Engineering**

And the following aspects of dispute:

### Category B – Nature of Dispute

☐ Design
☐ Electrical Services
☐ Latent Defects
☐ Mechanical Services
☐ Research
☐ Valuation/Quantum

☐ Consultancy/Professional Services
☐ Insurance
☐ Legal/Contractual
☐ Project/Contract Management
☐ Risk/Value Management

☐ Delay and Disruption
☐ Investigations
☐ Maintenance
☐ Quality/Specification
☐ Temporary Works

The Arbitrator should have a knowledge of the following types of work:

### Category C – Type of Work

☐ Bridges
☐ Buildings
☐ Construction Materials
☐ Demolition
☐ Earthworks
☐ Energy and Power
☐ Environmental Engineering
☐ Fire Engineering
☐ Foundations/Substructures
☐ Geotechnical

☐ Health and Safety
☐ Highways and Transport
☐ Marine Engineering
☐ Mineral Extraction
☐ Municipal
☐ Structural Design
☐ Tunnelling
☐ Water and Sewerage
☐ **Other** (Please Specify Below) ↓

**Comment on work category (if required by the Applicant)**

**Notes:**

- In most cases a working knowledge of a work category is required by an Arbitrator. The applicant should state here if any very specialist knowledge is required.
- **In exceptional circumstances** a particular subdivision of a work category may be included i.e. for **Foundations/Substructures** the subdivision might be **bored piling**.

**If key words or work categories are unsuitable please describe any specialist knowledge required.**

. . . . . . . . . . . . . . . . . . . . . . . . . . . . . . . . . . . . . . . . . . . . . . . . . . . . . . . . . . . . . . . . . . . . . . . . . . . . . . . . . . . . . . . . . . . . . . . . . . . .

**Appointment of an Arbitrator by the President of the Institution of Civil Engineers**

From the President:

To:

I hereby appoint:

of

as requested

Dated:

**President/Vice-President**

Copies for information:

    The Appointed

    The Parties (other than the Applicant)